THE X FILES™

CREATED BY CHRIS CARTER

Project Aquarius
and other stories

Story
Stefan Petrucha

Art
Charles Adlard

THE X-FILES
PROJECT AQUARIUS

Created by Chris Carter
Story by Stefan Petrucha
Art by Charles Adlard
Colours by George Freeman & Laurie E Smith
Lettering by John Workman

Cover and Chapter Heading Illustrations by Miran Kim

Published by Manga Publishing Ltd., 40 St Peters Road, London W6 9BD.
First edition published July 1996. No part of this publication may
be reproduced or transmitted by any means, electronic, mechanical,
photocopying or otherwise, without the prior permission of the Publisher.

British Library Cataloguing in Publication Date. A catalogue record for
this book is available from the British Library.

ISBN 1 900097 17 6

Printed in Great Britain.

THE X FILES™

CONTENTS

THE HOPEWELL ORPHANAGE
LEWISTON, MAINE
DECEMBER 21, 1954
4:54 P.M.

NOW THAT YOU'RE DEAD, MULDER AND SCULLY AND DRAKE, AS DEAD AS THE TREES IN DECEMBER, MAYBE YOU CAN UNDERSTAND WHAT IT IS THAT I AM.

THE SUN WAS ALMOST GONE. THE SOFT SNOW WAS TURNING TO ICE, WHICH MADE FOR A FASTER RIDE.

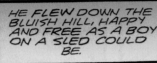

HE FLEW DOWN THE BLUISH HILL, HAPPY AND FREE AS A BOY ON A SLED COULD BE.

UNTIL HE SAW THE LIGHT.

THERE WAS NO WAY HE COULD **STOP.**

THERE WAS NO WAY THE **CAR** COULD STOP.

HE **KNEW** HE WAS GOING TO **DIE.**

THE FRIGHTENED **DRIVER** SCREAMED AND CURSED AT HIM, BUT THE BOY DIDN'T **CARE**— HE WAS **ALIVE.**

WASN'T HE?

LATER, AS HE LAY IN BED, HE **WONDERED** IF EVERYTHING SINCE THAT MOMENT MIGHT BE A **DREAM,** IF HE MIGHT **STILL** BE SLIDING DOWN THAT HILL, HEADING TOWARDS THOSE LIGHTS, JUST **IMAGINING** HE HAD A **LIFE** TO LEAD.

WHEN HE REALIZED THERE WAS NO WAY HE COULD EVER **KNOW** FOR CERTAIN, **I** WAS BORN.

TREPANATION, OR, THE MODERN, *TREPHINATION*, IS THE WORLD'S *OLDEST* FORM OF *SURGERY.*

FOR MILLENNIA, PEOPLE HAVE BEEN DRILLING HOLES IN THEIR SKULLS-- TO LET DEVILS *OUT,* LIGHT *IN,* SOMETIMES...

...JUST TO RELIEVE *HEAD-ACHES.*

SOME MYSTICS BELIEVE EXPOSING THE *THIRD EYE* PIERCES *MAYA* LIFE'S *ILLUSION* ALLOWING ACCESS TO *PURE TRUTH.*

THE *PINEAL GLAND* IS ASSOCIATED WITH THE *THIRD EYE.* IN SOME REPTILES AND BIRDS, IT IS LIGHT-SENSITIVE, ACTING LITERALLY AS A *THIRD EYE.* IN HUMANS, IT IS LOCATED IN THE MIDDLE OF THE BROW.

IN THE '60s, UNABLE TO FIND WILLING SURGEONS, SOME FOLLOWERS OF DOCTOR BART HUGHES TREPANNED *THEMSELVES.*

THEY REPORTED AN EXPERIENCE AKIN TO A PERPETUAL LSD TRIP, INCLUDING UNUSUAL *PSYCHIC* ABILITIES.

GIVEN THE *LOCATION* OF THE WOUNDS, I BELIEVE OUR KILLER...A *TREPANNER* HIMSELF...WANTS TO *SHARE* HIS EXPERIENCE.

TREPANNING, FOR *BELIEVERS,* IS A *GIFT* THAT KEEPS ON GIVING.

BUT THAT'S ONLY *HALF* THE STORY-- AGENT DRAKE?

THIS TIME OUT, A *LETTER* WAS FOUND ON THE BODY.

ANALYSIS REVEALED THAT IT WAS WRITTEN IN THREE *CODED* PARTS. A *KEY WORD* IS NEEDED TO READ EACH PART.

THE FIRST, EASILY ENOUGH, WAS *"MULDER."*

HAKJHD IAKJH AJH LKEJKMN
LASMP YAOME OSKE UMMEN
XSMND POMNEL HKJRELK INM
LDNBEL ELKW SMAP OSMKND
UOIEUU TKNEB TWKNWMNN
ENB EKJWOLLKJ RTHG EOPTH

OUR FRIEND BELIEVES THAT, UNLIKE US WORKING STIFFS, HE LIVES *BACKWARDS* AND *FORWARDS* IN TIME.

HE GOES ON TO CAREFULLY DESCRIBE, IN THE PAST TENSE, A *MURDER* WHICH HASN'T OCCURRED *--YET.*

AS FOLLOWS...

WHEN HE REALIZED THERE WAS NO WAY HE COULD EVER KNOW FOR CERTAIN, IN THAT MOMENT, I WAS BORN.

THE WORLD YOU KNOW IS FALSE-- THE *DREAM* OF A BOY ON A HILL SLIDING TO HIS *DEATH.* I AM HERE TO AWAKEN YOU FROM THE *DREAM,* ONE BY ONE BY ONE. BY *SHREDDING* WHAT YOU THINK IS REAL...YOUR MIND, YOUR BODY, YOUR *LIFE.*

IT WAS NICE AND HOT ON JULY 15, 1995. THE TEMPERATURE HIT **85.7** DEGREES AT NOON.

HAVING JUST MISSED HIS MAILMAN, A *SIGHTLESS* MAN TOOK A STROLL TO POST HIS MONTHLY BILLS.

BEING QUITE ADEPT AT SENSING THE PRESENCE OF OTHERS, HE WAS STARTLED AT FIRST BY MY *NEARNESS.*

BUT *PART* OF HIM KNEW THAT THE *WORST* WOULD BE OVER SOON, AND A WHOLE NEW WORLD WOULD *OPEN* UP TO HIM.

HE DIDN'T STRUGGLE AT ALL, REALLY.

AND THE *PHARMACY* WAS SO *CROWDED.* ANYONE MIGHT HAVE HEARD. THE NUMBER OF THE BUILDING WAS 1586.

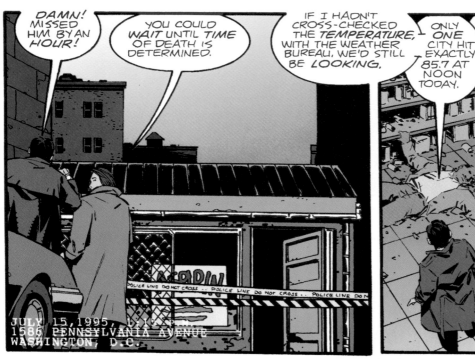

DAMN! MISSED HIM BY AN HOUR!

YOU COULD *WAIT* UNTIL *TIME* OF DEATH IS DETERMINED.

IF I HADN'T CROSS-CHECKED THE *TEMPERATURE* WITH THE WEATHER BUREAU, WE'D STILL BE *LOOKING.*

ONLY *ONE* CITY EXACTLY HIT 85.7 AT NOON TODAY.

YOU DON'T *REALLY* THINK HE CAN TELL THE *FUTURE,* DO YOU?

JULY 15, 1995, 1:15 P.M.
1586 PENNSYLVANIA AVENUE
WASHINGTON, D.C.

WELL, HE'S GOT MY WEATHER-MAN BEAT.

AND HOW ELSE CAN WE EXPLAIN THE DETAILS HE GAVE *BEFORE* THE FACT? HOW DID HE KNOW OUR NAMES?

WHAT ABOUT ACCESS TO THE *FBI REGISTRY?* OR THE *FARMER'S ALMANAC?* WHAT IF HE *STALKS* HIS VICTIMS AND LEARNS THEIR *HABITS?*

THE *MELATONIN* PRODUCED BY THE PINEAL GLAND CONTROLS OUR BIOLOGICAL SENSE OF *TIME,* BUT TO CLAIM THAT EXPOSING THE BRAIN CAN ALLOW SOMEONE TO SEE THE FUTURE IS *ABSURD.*

WHAT *SHE* SAID SOUNDED GOOD TO *ME,* BIG GUY.

OKAY.

SCULLY

BUT WHY DON'T WE SEE WHAT *HE* HAS TO SAY ABOUT IT?

OF ALL THE TYPES OF BLINDNESS, MY FAVORITE IS FEAR-INDUCED. FEAR IS MYOPIC. IT CAN'T ACCEPT THE UNKNOWN.

THAT'S YOUR BLINDNESS, SCULLY. THE SKEPTIC'S BLINDNESS.

YOU WORKED FOR SIX HOURS, WRACKING YOUR MIND FOR LOGICAL POSSIBILITIES.

YOU TRIED TO WORK FOR SEVEN, JUST TO PROVE THIS MESSAGE WRONG--BUT YOU LOST TRACK OF TIME.

ALL YOU FOUND WAS A SMILE.

AND ALL THE WHILE, THE COMPUTERS DREAMED OF ZEROES AND ONES --UNABLE TO IMAGINE A TWO.

WE'VE GOT TO CRACK THAT THIRD SEGMENT. WE NEED MORE MANPOWER.

SOMETHING ELSE ON YOUR MIND, AGENT MULDER?

YES. YOU'VE RUN BACKGROUND CHECKS ON EVERY-ONE. SCULLY AND I KNOW--WITH NO LUCK.

YOU'RE WASTING RESOURCES --AND TIME!

CAN'T YOU AT LEAST ACKNOWL-EDGE THE POSSIBILITY THERE'S SOME-THING OPER-ATING HERE WE DON'T UNDER-STAND?

HEY, THERE'S LOTS I DON'T UN-DERSTAND, OKAY? BUT WE'VE DRAINED THE SECOND SEG-MENT DRY--WITHOUT A CLUE --PSYCHIC OR OTHERWISE,

AND WHILE YOU'RE BUSY DEFENDING YOUR INANE MYSTI-CISM--SOMEONE'S BEING KILLED OUT THERE!

SO SUE ME IF I WANT TO COVER ALL THE POSSIBILITIES.

"OKAY, DRAKE, MAYBE YOU'RE RIGHT. LET'S TRY IT AGAIN. PAGE ONE."

WHEN THE BLIND LEADS THE BLIND, THEY FALL TO-GETHER IN THE DITCH. THAT'S WHY I AM SO OFTEN WEL-COMED.

THIS TIME, THE DREAM OF THE WORLD WAS SO COMFORTABLE, THE DARK SO SOOTH-ING...

...HE WALKED RIGHT PAST THE DOOR TO HIS AWAKENING...

...UNABLE TO RECOG-NIZE IT FOR WHAT IT WAS.

FIRST I TOOK HIS SANCTUARY, LEAVING HIM FEELING QUITE NAKED.

THEN I TOOK HIS FAMILY, LEAVING HIM FEELING QUITE ALONE.

THEN I TOOK HIS BODY...

LEAVING HIM FEELING QUITE AFRAID.

LASTLY, I TOOK HIS HEAD.

WIRRRRRRRR

AS HE SCREAMED, I WAS THINKING, WHAT IS IT THAT A MAN IS? A HUSBAND? A FATHER? A SHADOW THAT SHRIVELS IN LIGHT?

YOU'LL BE NEXT. OR SHOULD I SAY YOU WERE FIRST?

JULY 16, 10 P.M. THE HOME OF AGENT FOX MULDER

IF THERE'S A LEAD IN THERE, I COULDN'T FIND IT. MAYBE YOU'RE RIGHT. MAYBE HE'S JUST SCHIZ.

DON'T TELL ME, TELL DRAKE!

HE'S WORKED ON THIS A LONG TIME, AND HE'S SMARTING BECAUSE HE HAS TO SHARE THE CASE WITH US.

NOT EVERYONE'S A VISIONARY, MULDER.

AND VISIONARIES AREN'T ALWAYS RIGHT.

AH, I NEED THIS LIKE I NEED A...

E FLAT?

*X-FILES # 2.

DRAKE WAS A DISAPPOINT-MENT--HE DIED WITH A WHIMPER. IT WAS SCULLY THAT PROVIDED THE CHALLENGE.

JULY 17, ROUGHLY 4 A.M. THEY WERE DRIVING ALONG *395* TOWARDS THE BRIDGE THAT CROSSES EAST POTOMAC PARK.

GLAD WE GOT A CHANCE TO *TALK.* I GUESS YOU CAN TELL WORKING WITH MULDER HASN'T BEEN *EASY* FOR ME.

SO I WANTED TO *THANK* YOU FOR TRYING TO MAKE THIS "TEAM" FUNCTION SMOOTHLY.

AND FOR NOT MENTIONING MY *TOUPEE.*

OH, THAT'S OKAY.

I GUESS *MOST* WEAR THEM OUT OF *VANITY.*

ME, I PICKED AN OBVIOUS *RUG.* I FIGURED IT MIGHT STOP FOLKS FROM NOTICING THE *LATEX* ON MY *FOREHEAD.*

...THAT I USE TO COVER *THIS!*

IT IS THE SIGN OF *LIGHT*. THE SIGN OF MY FATHER'S *LOVE*. THEIR NAME WAS *BIERCE*.

THEY TOOK HIM AWAY--PUT THE BOY IN AN *ORPHANAGE*.

UNTIL HE ALMOST FORGOT HIS *REAL* NAME, UNTIL HE ALMOST FORGOT WHAT HE COULD *SEE*.

BUT IT'S ALL RIGHT NOW. IT DOESN'T MATTER IF HE'S BIERCE OR DRAKE-- HE'S MELTED INTO *ME* NOW--AND I HAVE NO NAME.

DRAKE, *LISTEN* TO ME. THAT STORY *CAN'T* BE TRUE. HOW DID YOU GET INTO THE *FBI*?

THEY DO *EXTENSIVE* BACKGROUND CHECKS.

BECAUSE LIFE IS BUT A *DREAM*. BECAUSE I WAS *INVITED*.

THEY WERE *ANGELS* WHEN THEY CAME TO ME, LORDS OF *LIGHT*, WHITE HORSES LEAPING FROM OCEAN FOAM.

THEY SAID THEY COULD *HELP* ME IF I WOULD HELP *THEM*.

AT FIRST THEIR REQUESTS WERE *SIMPLE*, BUT THEN THEY WANTED A HAND IN PICKING MY *SUBJECTS*.

THEN THEY WANTED *MULDER* TO SEE THE LIGHT. I AGREED, BUT ONLY IF I COULD BRING IT TO *YOU* FIRST.

IT'S SO MUCH SWEETER WHEN *SKEPTICS* FACE THE *TRUTH*.

AND LIKE A **TRUE** SKEPTIC, LIKE ANY-ONE **ENRAPTURED** BY THE DARK, SHE **FOUGHT** THE LIGHT TO THE LAST.

YOU DON'T KNOW WHAT IT'S LIKE TO SEE THE BIRTHING OF A **SOUL** INTO THE TRUTH.

THE **LIGHT** IN HER OPENED LIKE A **FLOWER.**

BLINDING EVEN **ME.**

"DON'T BE A **FOOL!**" I SAID, "I WON'T KILL YOU BEFORE YOU ARE **ENLIGHTENED!**"

BUT **I** WAS THE FOOL.

SHE WAS THE **TEACHER.**

TREPHINATION PROVIDES A CONTINUAL PEAK, BUT AT THE MOMENT OF DEATH, THE HEART POUNDING, THE BLOOD RUSHING TO THE BRAIN--IT'S EXACTLY THE SAME.

YOU SHOULD HAVE SEEN IT. IT WAS SO BEAUTIFUL.

THE DOOR OPENED AND SHE WENT IN, UNAFRAID.

SHE AWOKE ON HER OWN TERMS--WITHOUT ME.

YOU WOULD HAVE BEEN SO PROUD.

I KNOW IT HURTS YOU, MULDER. I KNOW YOU'RE MOURNING SCULLY.

YOU FEEL AS THOUGH SOMETHING'S BEEN LOST, BUT IT HASN'T BEEN.

ALL THIS PAIN, HUNGER, AND DESPERATION--IT'S JUST A GAME WE PLAY, A DREAM.

CAN'T YOU SEE? THESE SAD LITTLE FORMS COULD NEVER HOLD US! IT'S ABSURD!

MULDER, WE ARE THE STUFF OF STARS!

YOU'LL SEE.

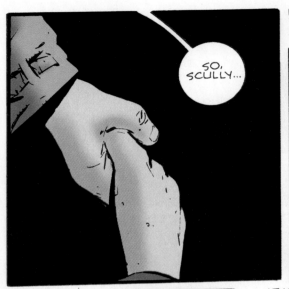

YOU MAY ONLY BE IMAGINING THAT YOU SURVIVED...

·THE END·

MT. ST. ELIAS, ALASKA
AUGUST 10

ONCE UPON A TIME, THE *MEXICA* SOUGHT A MARRIAGE WITH THE *TOLTECS*. THE TOLTECS AGREED AND PRESENTED THE MEXICA WITH THEIR KING'S *DAUGHTER*.

BUT WHEN THE TOLTEC KING ARRIVED FOR THE CEREMONY, HE WAS GREETED BY A MEXICA PRIEST DRESSED IN HIS DAUGHTER'S *SKIN*.

WAS SHE *GONE?*

THE MEXICA MIGHT SAY THE PRIEST HAD *BECOME* HER.

LIKEWISE, IF ALL PUAKABALAUA WAS WITHIN *ME* NOW, IS HE *GONE* OR HAVE I *BECOME* HIM?

I'M SORRY, I HAVE TO *GO.*

THE HERON HAS FINISHED EATING THE SNAKE AND I THINK IT WANTS ME TO *FOLLOW.* HEH-HEH.

ENOCH! ENOCH, COME IN! GIVE US YOUR LOCATION!

ENOCH, THIS IS MOTHER--

BLAM!

HEH, CAN'T MEASURE *TRUTH* THAT WAY, MULDER. ONE SIZE FITS ALL.

WE *KNOW* HOW THIS WILL END--AND WE WANT *OUR* SIDE TOLD. BUT FIRST, A *QUESTION.* CALL IT A *TEST* IF YOU LIKE.

WHERE WILL THE CHRONICLES OF *ATLANTIS* BE FOUND?

IF I'D *KNOWN* WE WERE GOING TO PLAY TRIVIAL PURSUIT, I'D HAVE BROUGHT MY *CARDS.*

ACCORDING TO *EDGAR CAYCE,* THEY'RE BURIED BETWEEN THE PAWS OF THE EGYPTIAN SPHINX. RECENT SONAR SOUNDINGS REVEALED SEVERAL *CHAMBERS.*

NO ONE'S *DUG* THEM UP *YET,* TO MY KNOWLEDGE.

YOU KNOW THAT *BIO-LOGICAL* DATA IS STORED IN DNA?

ONTOGENY RECAPITULATES PHYLOGENY. WE ALL HAVE *GILLS* IN THE *WOMB.*

WE BELIEVE *EVERYTHING* AN INDIVIDUAL *KNOWS* AND *IS,* IS *ALSO* RECORDED IN OUR *BODIES.*

IF THE RAW MATERIAL IS *INGESTED* UNDER THE PROPER CIRCUMSTANCES...

...THE INFORMATION CAN BE *CONSCIOUSLY* ABSORBED.

ENOCH WAS CONVINCED THAT THE ANCIENTS *KNEW* THE SECRET-- THAT THE KNOWLEDGE RESIDED SPECIFICALLY WITH ONE OF THE *LOST TRIBES* OF THE HEBREWS.

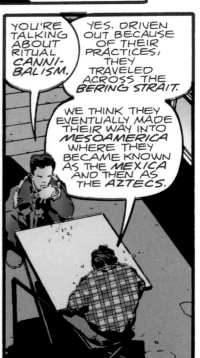

YOU'RE TALKING ABOUT RITUAL *CANNI-BALISM.*

YES, DRIVEN OUT BECAUSE OF THEIR PRACTICES, THEY TRAVELED ACROSS THE *BERING STRAIT.*

WE THINK THEY EVENTUALLY MADE THEIR WAY INTO *MESOAMERICA* WHERE THEY BECAME KNOWN AS THE *MEXICA* AND THEN AS THE *AZTECS.*

"ABOUT SIX MONTHS AGO, DR. ENOCH RECEIVED AN OFFER TO FUND AN EXPEDITION TO PROVE HIS THEORIES."

"HE BECAME NERVOUS, REFUSED TO DISCUSS IT, EXCEPT TO SAY THE SOURCE WAS HIGH-LEVEL, TOP SECRET.

"AFTER HE LEFT, OUR PHONES WERE TAPPED. STRANGERS WERE SPOTTED ON OUR PROPERTY ALMOST DAILY.

"SOME CLAIMED TO BE FEDERAL AGENTS-- BUT WE COULD NEVER CONFIRM THEIR IDENTITIES. WE ARMED AND PRE-PARED FOR THE WORST."

THE LAST CONTACT WE HAD FROM DOCTOR ENOCH WAS THIS FAX.

WE ARE EACH OF US A WORLD, OUR BODIES THE FIRMAMENT, OUR SOULS THE SKY, OUR BARBARIC HEARTS HELD AT BAY BY THE SILENT CITIES OF THE MIND.

I DON'T LIKE THIS AT ALL. HE'S BEEN IN THERE FOR *HOURS.*

RELAX, *AGENT SCULLY.* MULDER CAN TAKE CARE OF HIMSELF.

HERE'S THE CORONER'S REPORT YOU ASKED FOR ON THOSE *BODIES* WE FOUND ON THE PROPERTY.

THIS INDICATES THERE'S EVIDENCE OF *CAN-NIBALISM!* WE'VE GOT TO GET MULDER *OUT* OF THERE *NOW!*

"WE MAY HAVE CROSSED SOME LINES HERE, MULDER.

"BUT THERE ARE *DARKER* FORCES AT WORK."

KSH

"COULD YOU JUST ANSWER ONE QUESTION FOR ME?"

"WHAT KIND OF MEAT IS IN THAT SANDWICH?"

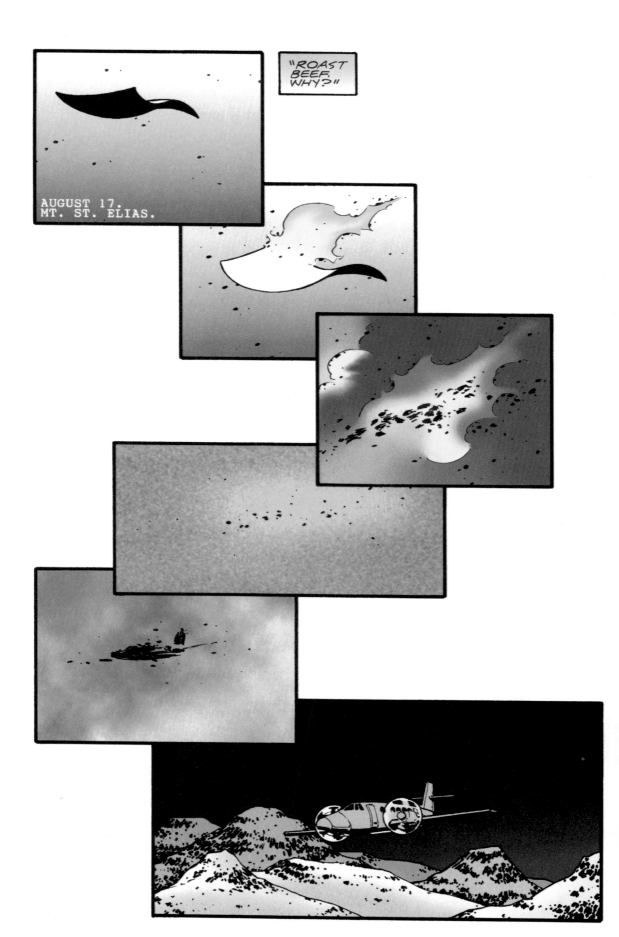

AUGUST 17.
MT. ST. ELIAS.

"ROAST
BEEF.
WHY?"

THERE IT IS, SCULLY. MOUNT SAINT ELIAS.

IN THE SUMMER OF 1897, THE DUKE OF ABRUZZI LED AN EX-PEDITION HERE TO FIND THE OFT-SIGHTED AND OCCASIONALLY PHOTOGRAPHED "*SILENT CITY OF ALASKA*."

FOR *YEARS*, PROSPECTORS AND LOCALS REPORTED SEEING A HUGE *METROPOLIS* WITH BUILDINGS AND STREETS.

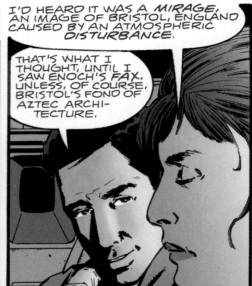

I'D HEARD IT WAS A *MIRAGE*, AN IMAGE OF BRISTOL, ENGLAND CAUSED BY AN ATMOSPHERIC *DISTURBANCE*.

THAT'S WHAT I THOUGHT, UNTIL I SAW ENOCH'S *FAX*. UNLESS, OF COURSE, BRISTOL'S FOND OF AZTEC ARCHI-TECTURE.

HOW'RE THE *REPORTS*?

BIZARRE.

THE RECOVERED NOTES BY ENOCH'S FOLLOWERS MAKE SOME HIGHLY IMPLAUSIBLE CLAIMS. EATING A *MUSICIAN* ENABLED THEM TO PLAY PIANO. EATING A *LINGUIST* MADE THEM FLUENT IN FRENCH.

OMPH! SOUNDS LIKE A REAL *PARTY*.

EVEN IF TRUE, SPONTANEOUS MUSICAL ABILITY IS WELL-DOCUMENTED IN SO-CALLED *IDIOT SAVANTS* AND THEY DIDN'T HAVE TO EAT *ANYONE*.

THE SAME WITH SPEAK-ING IN *TONGUES*.

SOME OF THE STRANGER *VISIONARY* TRACTS BY ENOCH MAY BE THE RESULT OF *KURU*--A RARE NEUROLOGICAL DISEASE SOME BELIEVE IS TRANSMITTED BY EATING *BRAINS.*

A NERVOUS TITTER BEING *SYMPTOMATIC* OF THE LATER STAGES, IT'S BEEN NICKNAMED *"THE LAUGHING SICKNESS."*

AS FOR THE REST, WE *KNOW* ALL SORTS OF THINGS WE CAN'T ALWAYS ACCESS *CONSCIOUSLY.*

FOR YEARS, THE *BRIDEY MURPHY* STORY WAS CONSIDERED THE BEST CASE FOR *REINCARNATION*-- A YOUNG GIRL HAD TOTAL RECALL OF A LIFE AND CULTURE SHE'D NO *ACCESS* TO.

UNTIL A RESEARCHER FOUND OUT BRIDEY WAS THE NAME OF THE GIRL'S *NANNY.* SHE HEARD BRIDEY'S STORIES GROWING UP, BUT REMEMBERED THEM AS HER *OWN* EXPERIENCES.

MEMORY IS A POWERFUL, *ELUSIVE* THING--AND WE HAVE NO REAL IDEA OF *HOW* IT WORKS.

IT'S MORE COMFORTABLE TO BELIEVE IN *MAGIC* THAN TO CONTEMPLATE HOW *LITTLE* WE KNOW OUR SELVES.

WE'RE ALWAYS SO SURE THE TRUTH IS *OUTSIDE,* WE'RE AFRAID TO LOOK *WITHIN.*

M-MULDER!

YOUR FOLLOWERS ARE DEAD OR IN PRISON.

YES, I KNOW. SOME KIND OF *EXPLOSION*?

YOU MUST HAVE BEEN TELLING THE *PILOT* ABOUT IT-- THE *FRESHEST* MEMORIES ARE ALWAYS THE FIRST *RECOVERED*.

HEH. FOR INSTANCE, WHEN *DR. PUAKABALAUA* DIED...

LOOK AT ME, I'M ABOUT TO TELL ANOTHER *STORY*.

I'M VERY FOND OF STORIES. I THINK *FICTION* CONTAINS A SORT OF *TRUTH* THAT HISTORY LACKS --DO YOU *MIND*?

UH, NO.

WELL, WHEN *DOCTOR PUAKABALAUA* DIED, HE WAS THINKING ABOUT SOME *ABO- RIGINES* HE'D STUDIED.

DURING WWII, AN AIR BASE WAS BUILT NEAR THEIR LAND. WHEN THEY SAW THE GREAT METAL *BIRDS* LANDING THERE, THEY ASSUMED THEY WERE *GODS*.

AND THE WHITE MEN WERE *STEALING* THE TREASURES THAT *RIGHTFULLY* BE- LONGED TO THE *TRIBE*.

DO YOU KNOW WHAT THEY *DID*?

THEY CLEARED A *RUN- WAY* AND BUILT A *RADAR TOWER* OUT OF *ROCKS* AND *BAMBOO*. EVEN BUILT THEIR OWN *MOCK AIRPLANE* FROM TWIGS AND LEAVES.

THE AIR BASE WAS LONG AGO *ABANDONED*, BUT TO THIS DAY THAT TRIBE SITS THERE IN THEIR FAKE *AIRPORT* AND WAITS FOR THE *GODS* TO LAND.

THEY SAW SOMETHING THEY DIDN'T UNDERSTAND AND TRIED TO *IMITATE* IT.

WELL, AS HE DIED, HEH, *DOCTOR PUAKA- BALAUA* WAS THINK- ING THAT THE PEOPLE WHO CAME *HERE* MUST HAVE SEEN SOMETHING, TOO. SOMETHING QUITE *EXTRAORDINARY*.

UHM.

"ACCORDING TO THEIR MYTHOLOGY, THE AZTECS CAME FROM A NORTHERN CITY CALLED *AZTLAN,* 'LAND OF THE HERONS.'

"AT FIRST WE THOUGHT *THIS* WAS AZTLAN, BUT THERE WERE TOO MANY DISCREPANCIES.

"THE PICTOGRAMS PLACE CONSTRUCTION SQUARELY IN THE REIGN OF *MOETE-ZUMA II,* THE LAST AZTEC EMPEROR.

"AND AZTLAN WAS A CITY SURROUNDED BY *WATER,* DESIGNED IN A SERIES OF *RINGS.* THE ACCOUNTS RESEMBLE PLATO'S DE-SCRIPTION OF *ATLANTIS.* AZTLAN. ATLANTIS.

"DOCTOR PUAKABALAUA ACTUALLY BELIEVED THAT THE AZTECS MAY HAVE COME FROM ATLANTIS.

"IMAGINE, HIM MAKING FUN OF *MY* THEORIES THEN TURNING AROUND AND BELIEVING IN *ATLANTIS.*

"HEH.

"DID YOU KNOW THAT SOME OF THE WORLD'S *LEADING* EGYPTOLOGISTS, IMMINENTLY RESPECTED, HAD THEIR EDUCATIONS PAID FOR BY THE *EDGAR CAYCE* INSTITUTE?

"I DIDN'T KNOW THAT, *EITHER.* UNTIL I ATE DR. PUAKABALUA.

"STILL, MY METHODS ARE VERY *CRUDE.*

"I GRASP A THOUGHT HERE AND THERE, GAIN A SKILL OR TWO, BUT IT'S SO *OVERWHELMING,* I GET A SORT OF INDIGESTION.

"EVEN NOW, I HAVE A HARD TIME DISTINGUISHING DR. PUAKABALAUA'S THOUGHTS FROM THOSE...

"THOSE OF..."

YOU *LIED* TO ME.

THERE *WAS* SOMEONE ELSE ON BOARD.

DANA SCULLY?

AGHHH!

DO YOU THINK IT MATTERS THAT I *REPULSE* YOU?

ONE DAY, WHEN *I* AM EATEN, MY *DEVOURER* WILL KNOW ME AS A *GREAT* MAN.

SHE'S *DEAD*, IN ANY CASE. THE PILOT SAW HER FALL FROM THE CABIN. IT'S *COLD* OUT, I'M SURE SHE'LL *KEEP.*

FOR DAYS, I'VE GRAPPLED WITH THE *SECRETS* OF THIS PLACE.

I MET A *HERON* I'D HOPED WOULD PROVIDE THE ANSWER, BUT IT WAS ONLY INTERESTED IN PROPHECY.

PERHAPS IT *KNEW* WHAT I WANTED, BUT *WOULDN'T* SAY. PERHAPS IT WAS ONLY A PTARMIGAN.

I ASKED IT, WHY WOULD ANYONE BUILD AN UNDER-GROUND CITY THAT PROJECTS ITSELF AS A *MIRAGE?*

ALL IT SAID WAS, "WHAT IS THE HOME OF MAN?" HEH.

THIS IS THE ONLY DOOR I CAN'T OPEN.

BE A GOOD FELLOW AND GIVE ME A *HAND* WITH IT.

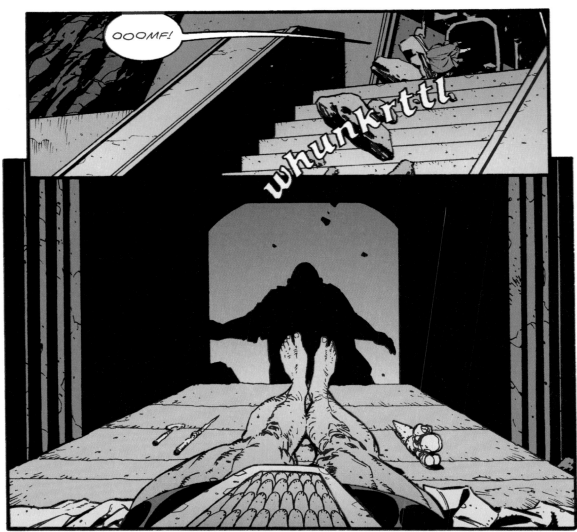

AUGUST 18
DAWN
MT. ST. ELIAS

HUSTLE WITH THOSE *EXPLOSIVES,* MEN.

I WANT A *BACK-UP* IN CASE DR. ENOCH STILL PROVES *RETICENT* ABOUT MAKING HIS AGREED-UPON *DELIVERY.*

I'M SURE HE'S GROWN QUITE *FOND* OF THIS PLACE. I INTEND TO USE THAT *AGAINST* HIM.

AFTER ALL, *HE* DOESN'T HAVE TO KNOW WE'LL BE USING THEM *REGARDLESS.*

SO, WOULD YOU LIKE TO HEAR WHAT *ELSE* ENOCH SAID?

EVEN THOUGH I DON'T ACCEPT THE *MODE* IN WHICH ENOCH *ACQUIRED* HIS INFORMATION, THAT DOESN'T MEAN I CAN CONCLUDE THE INFORMATION *ITSELF* IS FALSE.

SO, YES.

"LET'S SEE HOW MUCH I REMEMBER.

"THE AZTEC EMPEROR WAS OFTEN LOOKED TO FOR AUGURIES, PREDICTIONS OF THE FUTURE, WHICH CAME THROUGH DREAMS.

"SHORTLY AFTER THE TEMPLE TO TOCI BURNED DOWN, MOCTEZUMA II HAD SUCH A DREAM-- ABOUT SOME HALF-MEN, HALF-DEER.

"NEVER A CHEERFUL SORT, HE COULDN'T SHAKE THE FEELING OF DREAD THE DREAM GAVE HIM.

"AS FAR AS HE KNEW, HE WAS MASTER OF THE WORLD, BUT HE COULDN'T SHAKE THE SENSE IT WAS ALL ABOUT TO END."

"THEN ANOTHER ILL OMEN OCCURRED.

"A GROUP OF HUNTERS PRESENTED MOCTEZUMA WITH A STRANGE BIRD. IN ITS HEAD WAS A MIRROR THE STARS COULD BE SEEN IN.

"HIS DREAD BECAME SO GREAT, MOCTEZUMA DECIDED TO TRY TO FLEE THE WORLD AND TAKE REFUGE WITH THE GODS.

"AZTEC CULTURE WAS BUILT ON OLDER MAYAN TRADITIONS. THE MAYANS BELIEVED THE FIRST MEN COULD SEE AND SPEAK TO THE GODS.

"NOT WANTING EQUALS, THE GODS LIMITED HUMAN SIGHT. A LOT LIKE OUR OWN EDEN MYTH. THE MAYANS ALSO BELIEVED THIS ORIGINAL STATE OF MAN COULD BE RESTORED WITH AN 'ILBAL', A SEEING INSTRUMENT.

"ANYWAY...

"MOCTEZUMA WAS CERTAIN THAT THE SECRET OF THE ILBAL WAS TO BE FOUND WITH THEIR ANCESTORS IN AZTLAN, LEGENDARY HOME OF THE AZTECS.

"SO HE ASSEMBLED SIXTY OF THE BEST SORCERERS IN HIS KINGDOM AND SENT THEM ON A QUEST.

"PUBLICLY, THEY WERE TO INVITE AZTLAN TO JOIN MOCTEZUMA'S EMPIRE. PRIVATELY, THEY WERE TO FIND THE SECRET OF THE ILBAL AND CONSTRUCT ONE FOR HIM.

"SORT OF A PRE-COLUMBIAN CONSPIRACY.

"THE LAST SORCERERS WHO'D DISAPPOINTED MOCTEZUMA WERE CHAINED AND LEFT TO SLOWLY STARVE TO DEATH.

"ALL THEY'D DONE WAS DISAGREE WITH HIM ABOUT A COMET.

"SO THESE GUYS THREW THEMSELVES INTO THEIR TASK WITH GREAT APLOMB.

"UNFORTUNATELY, OTHER THAN SOMEWHERE NORTH, THEY DIDN'T HAVE THE SLIGHTEST IDEA WHERE AZTLAN WAS--SO THEY NEVER FOUND IT.

"JUST AS THEY WERE ABOUT TO CALL IT QUITS, THE ANSWER CAME TO THEM IN, YOU GUESSED IT, A VIVID DREAM.

"IN IT, THEY CHANGED INTO HERONS AND FLEW TO AZTLAN. THERE, LARGE-EYED WISE MEN GAVE THEM THE SECRET THEY WERE LOOKING FOR.

"FROM ENOCH'S DESCRIPTION, IT SOUNDS LIKE THEY HAD A CLASSIC ABDUCTION EXPERIENCE--COMPLETE WITH MISSING TIME. WE CAN ARGUE THE PARTICULARS LATER."

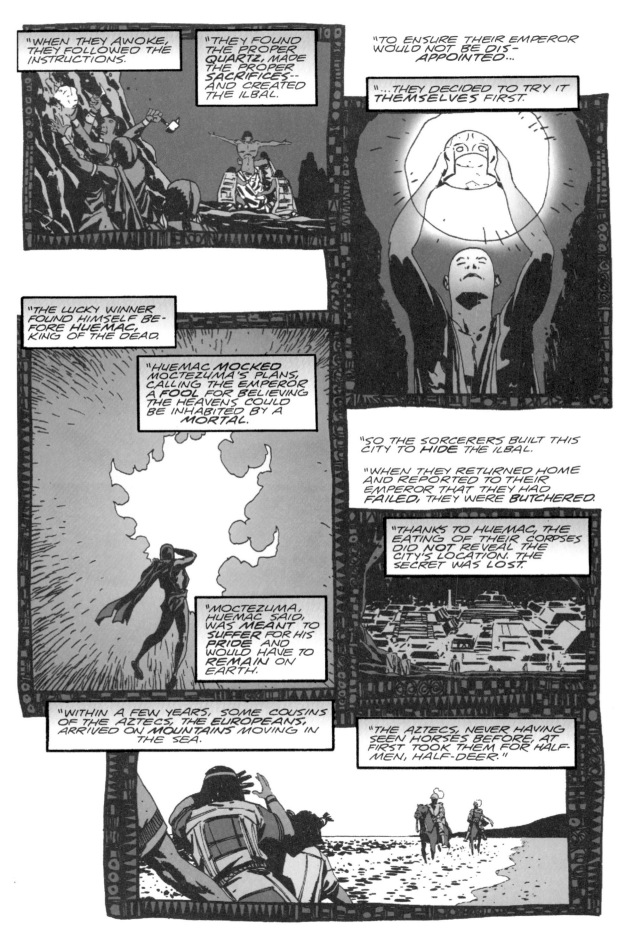

"WHEN THEY AWOKE, THEY FOLLOWED THE INSTRUCTIONS.

"THEY FOUND THE PROPER QUARTZ, MADE THE PROPER SACRIFICES-- AND CREATED THE ILBAL.

"TO ENSURE THEIR EMPEROR WOULD NOT BE DIS-APPOINTED...

"...THEY DECIDED TO TRY IT THEMSELVES FIRST.

"THE LUCKY WINNER FOUND HIMSELF BEFORE HUEMAC, KING OF THE DEAD.

"HUEMAC MOCKED MOCTEZUMA'S PLANS, CALLING THE EMPEROR A FOOL FOR BELIEVING THE HEAVENS COULD BE INHABITED BY A MORTAL.

"SO THE SORCERERS BUILT THIS CITY TO HIDE THE ILBAL.

"WHEN THEY RETURNED HOME AND REPORTED TO THEIR EMPEROR THAT THEY HAD FAILED, THEY WERE BUTCHERED.

"THANKS TO HUEMAC, THE EATING OF THEIR CORPSES DID NOT REVEAL THE CITY'S LOCATION. THE SECRET WAS LOST.

"MOCTEZUMA, HUEMAC SAID, WAS MEANT TO SUFFER FOR HIS PRIDE AND WOULD HAVE TO REMAIN ON EARTH.

"WITHIN A FEW YEARS, SOME COUSINS OF THE AZTECS, THE EUROPEANS, ARRIVED ON MOUNTAINS MOVING IN THE SEA.

"THE AZTECS, NEVER HAVING SEEN HORSES BEFORE, AT FIRST TOOK THEM FOR HALF-MEN, HALF-DEER."

CRK

HOLD FIRE!

THE GENERAL IS *DEAD.* SO IS *ENOCH.*

ANSWER *CAREFULLY,* AGENT. DO YOU HAVE THE *ILBAL?*

YES.

MY MISSION IS TO *RETRIEVE* IT. TURN IT *OVER,* ALONG WITH THE GENERAL'S PERSONAL *EFFECTS*--AND YOU'LL HAVE *ONE HOUR* TO LEAVE.

WHY SHOULD I *BELIEVE* YOU?

BECAUSE, AGENT MULDER, UNLIKE THE GENERAL, I *ADMIRE* YOUR WORK.

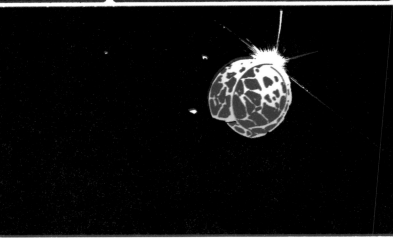

I CAN'T *BELIEVE* YOU GAVE THEM THAT *HELMET.*

THEY WERE PLANNING TO *KILL* US, SCULLY. IT WAS A *CALCULATED* RISK.

BESIDES, I THINK WE MAY HAVE SOMETHING *BETTER...*

IT'S ALL FALLING *TOGETHER* NOW. THE *SHADOWS* GROW *BRIGHTER* THAN THE *LIGHT.* HEH-HEH.

MULDER, LOOK AT HIM! HE'S *BADLY* WOUNDED, *BABBLING.* HE MAY NOT *SURVIVE* THE TRIP OUT OF HERE.

HE'S NOT OUR *KEY* TO ANYTHING!

YOU SAID *YOURSELF* THERE ARE MANY THINGS BURIED IN OUR SUBCON-SCIOUS THAT WE *KNOW* WITHOUT *REALIZING* IT.

DOCTOR ENOCH HAS DISPLAYED AN *UNCANNY* KNOWLEDGE ABOUT THIS PLACE.

THE AZTEC CAPITAL, *TENO-CHITLAN,* WAS BUILT, ON THE *ORDERS* OF A *GOD,* IN THE MIDDLE OF A *SWAMP,* SURROUNDED BY WATER...

...TO MAKE IT *RESEMBLE* THEIR LOST *HOME* AS MUCH AS POSSIBLE. HEH-HEH.

I ALSO SAID MEMORY WAS *NOTORIOUSLY* UNRELIABLE --AND I *NEVER* SAID *CAN-NIBALISM* WAS AN EFFECTIVE MODE OF INFORMATION RETRIEVAL.

BUT *BREAKING* SOCIAL TABOOS CAN TEAR DOWN CERTAIN WALLS WITHIN THE PSYCHE, NO?

FOR YEARS THE WATERS WERE *PEACEFUL.* UNTIL THE *SORCERERS* RETURNED.

AFTER AVOIDING FURTHER CONTACT WITH THE SOLDIERS, WE REACHED A STATE PARK OUTPOST TWO DAYS LATER.

UPON OUR RETURN, ENOCH WAS DIAGNOSED WITH KURU. THE DOCTORS HAVE GIVEN HIM LESS THAN A MONTH TO LIVE.

HE WILL BE TRIED POSTHUMOUSLY.

THE ENTRANCE HAS BEEN DESTROYED, MOTHER BASE SIX.

BUT I'M STILL WONDERING WHAT THE HELL AQUARIUS THINKS THIS HELMET *DOES.*

THOUGH ENOCH HAS BECOME INCREASINGLY INCOHERENT, AGENT MULDER SPENDS HOURS BY HIS SIDE IN THE BELIEF THAT HE MAY BE OUR LINK TO THE CONSPIRACY TO WHICH GENERAL SHADENFREUD BELONGED.

ALTHOUGH THERE IS LITTLE CHANCE KURU CAN BE CONTRACTED FROM SUCH CONTACT, THE LONG HOURS AGENT MULDER KEEPS MAKE ME CONCERNED FOR HIS HEALTH.

THIS IS MOTHER BASE SIX. JUST TAKE YOUR MEN *HOME,* COLONEL. IT'S NOT YOUR *JOB* TO WONDER.

TRUST NO ONE

"FOR SIX DAYS, I'VE BEEN LISTENING TO AN ENDLESS *STREAM* OF LANGUAGE PRODUCED BY A DYING MIND.

"DOCTOR ENOCH IS SUCCUMBING TO KURU, A DISEASE HE LIKELY CONTRACTED BY EATING HUMAN BRAINS.

"UNLIKE OTHER MODERN *CANNIBALS,* WHO ACT OUT OF A PERVERTED *SEXUAL* IMPULSE, HE DEVOURED HIS VICTIMS BELIEVING HE'D ACQUIRE THEIR *MEMORIES* AND *ABILITIES.*

"GIVEN THE INSIGHTS HE DISPLAYED IN *ALASKA**—SOME VERSION OF HIS THEORY MAY WELL BE *CORRECT.*

*AS REVEALED IN *THE X-FILES* #8-9.

"I'VE HEARD HIM SPEAK WITH THE VOICE OF AN *AZTEC PRIEST,* AN *ARCHEOLOGIST,* EVEN A *PIZZA BOY.*

"HIS *LAST MEAL* INTERESTS ME MOST: *GENERAL SHADEN-FREUD*—A MEMBER OF THE INNER GOVERNMENT WHOSE SECRETS I'VE WORKED SO HARD TO *UNLOCK.*

"IT IS, WITHOUT A DOUBT, THE MOST *UNUSUAL* TESTIMONY I'VE *EVER* TAKEN. I WOULDN'T BE SURPRISED IF MY NICKNAME CHANGED FROM 'SPOOKY' TO 'MAD.'

"BUT PERHAPS IN A WORLD WHERE *65%* OF THE POPULATION *BELIEVES* IN FLYING SAUCERS, AND UNOFFICIAL GOVERNMENT POLICY IS TO DENY *EVERYTHING*...

"...*MADNESS* IS THE BEGINNING OF *WISDOM.*"

FOR YOU...   ...FOR YOU...   ...FOR YOU...

ANTON WILSON HIGH SCHOOL
WASHINGTON, DC
OCTOBER 28, 1995
10 P.M.

GLAD YOU COULD MAKE IT, *SCULLY.* CLASS IS ABOUT TO *BEGIN.*

MULDER, ARE YOU ALL *RIGHT?* YOU LOOK AS THOUGH YOU HAVEN'T SLEPT IN DAYS!

WHAT IS IT WE COULDN'T DISCUSS AT THE *OFFICE?*

THE *ANSWERS,* SCULLY.

I THINK I'VE FINALLY GOT SOME OF THE *ANSWERS.*

GIVE ME A *MINUTE*. MY MIND DOESN'T RACE AS FAST AS YOURS, ESPECIALLY WHEN I'M WELL-RESTED. I *DO* HAVE FAITH IN YOU, MULDER. I TRUST YOU WITH MY *LIFE*. IT'S JUST...

IT'S JUST THAT, *ASIDE* FROM THE FACT THAT YOU'RE ASKING ME TO BELIEVE A *DELIRIOUS CANNIBAL*...

...I CAN'T GET PAST THE FACT THAT I CAN TAKE THE *SAME INFORMATION* AND DRAW A HUNDRED *DIFFERENT* CONCLUSIONS!

GIVE ME A CALL WHEN YOU *CATCH UP*.

YOU KNOW WHERE TO *REACH* ME.

OCTOBER 29, 1995
THE APARTMENT OF
AGENT FOX MULDER

OCTOBER 30, 1995
1:14 P.M.
THE REFLECTING POOL,
WASHINGTON DC

HA-HA!

COLLEEN KENT. MAIDEN NAME DUNNE.

I REMEMBER.

BRRRNG BRRRNG BRRRNG

I'VE BEEN *UNABLE* TO CONTACT AGENT MULDER.

SINCE THIS MATTER INVOLVES A POSSIBLE *BREACH* IN NATIONAL SECURITY, I'D LIKE PERMISSION TO *PROCEED* AND A *PRIORITY* DATABASE CLEARANCE.

PROCEED, THEN, AGENT SCULLY.

DOES THAT *INCLUDE* MY REQUESTED PRIORITY ACCESS, SIR?

PERMISSION TO PROCEED *INCLUDES* PERMISSION TO UTILIZE ANY RESOURCES *NECESSARY* TO PROCEED.

IS THAT *CLEAR*, AGENT SCULLY?

YES, SIR.

START WITH A *MARRIAGE CERTIFICATE,* LATE FORTIES, FOR A *JONAS KENT* AND *COLLEEN DUNNE* IN THE MID-WEST.

SHE'D BE AT LEAST IN HER *SEVENTIES* BY NOW. ALSO CHECK SOCIAL SECURITY, MEDICAID...

...AND ANY RECORDS OF LIVING RELATIONS TO *MILITARY PERSONNEL.*

I THINK I'VE GOT IT, AGENT SCULLY.

NAME:
DUNNE, COLLEEN
DATE OF BIRTH:
6·29·1927
CURRENT RESIDENCE:
GOTHIC ARMS
210 WEST 48TH STREET
NEW YORK, NEW YORK
NOTES:
HOMELESS HOTEL.
CHRONIC SCHIZOPHRENIC.
[MORE]

YES, WHEN'S YOUR NEXT FLIGHT TO *NEW YORK?*

GOT HER. SHE'S IN *NEW YORK.* ADDRESS TO FOLLOW.

HOW DID I GET HERE?

NEW YORK CITY

THE GOTHIC ARMS

THIS IS AGENT DANA SCULLY, ID NUMBER 2317-616.

I NEED *BACK-UP* AT THE GOTHIC ARMS HOTEL ON WEST 84TH STREET. THERE'S BEEN A *MURDER* AND THE PERPETRATORS MAY STILL BE PRESENT.

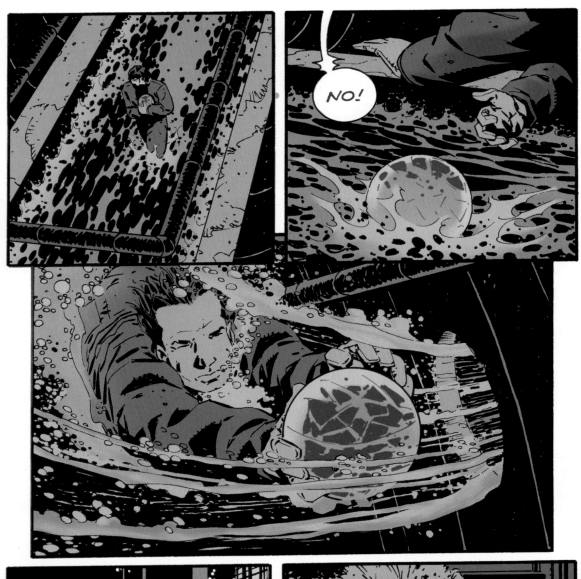

NO!

SKREE

FEELINGS OF UNREALITY - PART 2
THE ANCIENT OF DAYS
...THEN THE INTRUDER APPARENTLY VANISHED SOMEWHERE BETWEEN THE LAWN AND THE PARKING LOT.
EARLY TESTING OF THE BLOOD SAMPLES SHOWED HIGH LEVELS OF ADRENALINE, WHICH MAY ACCOUNT FOR HIS UNUSUAL STRENGTH.
HAPPY HALLOWEEN.
2:10 P.M.

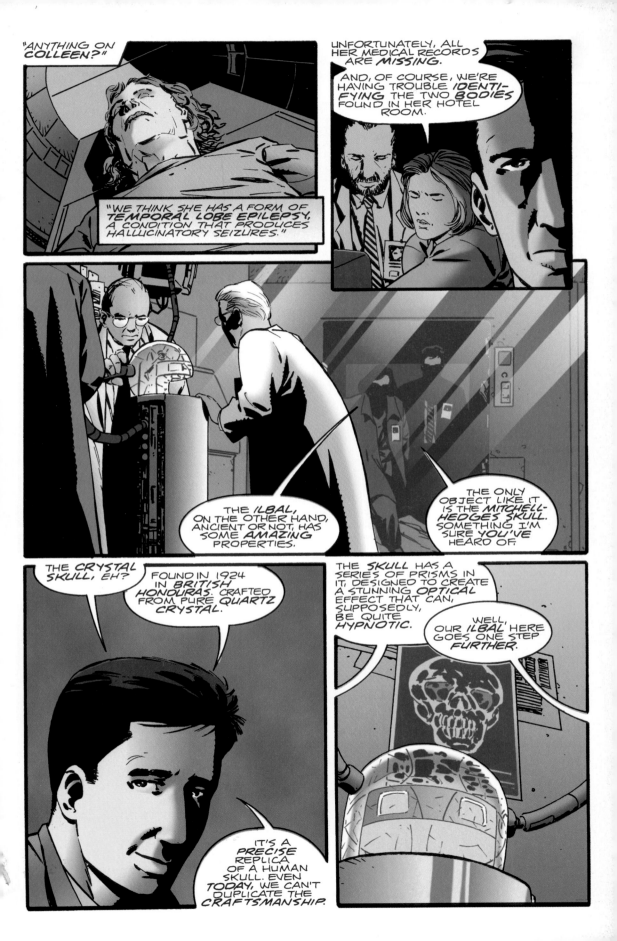

"ANYTHING ON COLLEEN?"

"WE THINK SHE HAS A FORM OF TEMPORAL LOBE EPILEPSY, A CONDITION THAT PRODUCES HALLUCINATORY SEIZURES."

UNFORTUNATELY, ALL HER MEDICAL RECORDS ARE MISSING.

AND, OF COURSE, WE'RE HAVING TROUBLE IDENTIFYING THE TWO BODIES FOUND IN HER HOTEL ROOM.

THE ILBAL, ON THE OTHER HAND, ANCIENT OR NOT, HAS SOME AMAZING PROPERTIES.

THE ONLY OBJECT LIKE IT IS THE MITCHELL-HEDGES SKULL. SOMETHING I'M SURE YOU'VE HEARD OF.

THE CRYSTAL SKULL, EH?

FOUND IN 1924 IN BRITISH HONDURAS. CRAFTED FROM PURE QUARTZ CRYSTAL.

IT'S A PRECISE REPLICA OF A HUMAN SKULL. EVEN TODAY, WE CAN'T DUPLICATE THE CRAFTSMANSHIP.

THE SKULL HAS A SERIES OF PRISMS IN IT, DESIGNED TO CREATE A STUNNING OPTICAL EFFECT THAT CAN, SUPPOSEDLY, BE QUITE HYPNOTIC.

WELL, OUR ILBAL HERE GOES ONE STEP FURTHER.

ALL QUARTZ HAS THE ABILITY TO *OSCILLATE*, MAKING IT USEFUL IN VARIOUS *ELECTRONIC* COMPONENTS.

THE ILBAL USES THAT PROPERTY TO CREATE A SERIES OF *RESONANT* OSCILLATIONS.

IN RESPONSE TO STIMULI, IT GENERATES ELECTROMAGNETIC PULSES...

SO IT LOOKS LIKE I *ALSO* MIGHT BE RIGHT ABOUT THE CONNECTION BETWEEN THIS AND THE *NEOLA* EXPERIMENTS.

MULDER, THERE'S SOMETHING I NEED TO SAY.

...THAT MIGHT BE INTENDED TO HAVE AN EFFECT ON *HUMAN BRAIN WAVES*.

FIRST OF ALL, I OWE YOU AN *APOLOGY*. IT'S OBVIOUS WE'VE COME ACROSS SOME KIND OF *CONSPIRACY*.

HEY, BE *CAREFUL!*

YOU START *AGREEING* WITH ME TOO MUCH, PRETTY SOON WE'LL HAVE *NOTHING* TO TALK ABOUT.

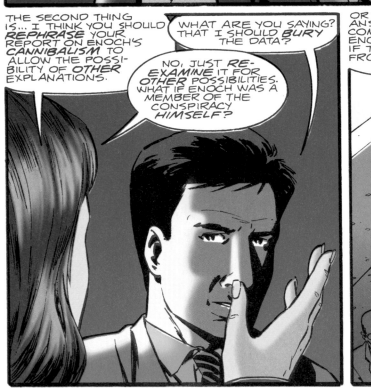

THE SECOND THING IS... I THINK YOU SHOULD *REPHRASE* YOUR REPORT ON ENOCH'S *CANNIBALISM* TO ALLOW THE POSSIBILITY OF *OTHER* EXPLANATIONS.

WHAT ARE YOU SAYING? THAT I SHOULD *BURY* THE DATA?

NO, JUST *REEXAMINE* IT FOR *OTHER* POSSIBILITIES. WHAT IF ENOCH WAS A MEMBER OF THE CONSPIRACY *HIMSELF?*

OR WHAT IF THE ANSWERS DIDN'T COME FROM ENOCH? WHAT IF THEY CAME FROM *YOU?*

SCIENTISTS OFTEN FIND *SOLUTIONS* TO PUZZLES IN *DREAMS* OR SUBTLE MESSAGES FROM THE *SUBCONSCIOUS*.

YOU'RE *OBSESSED* WITH THIS. YOU WERE *TIRED*, LISTENING TO *BABBLE*. WHAT IF YOU SUBCONSCIOUSLY *PROJECTED* MEANING ONTO IT AND DERIVED A CORRECT CONCLUSION?

THAT'S NOT WHAT *HAPPENED*, SCULLY. ENOCH HAD *ACCESS* TO SOMETHING THE REST OF US JUST *DON'T*.

BUT I UNDERSTAND YOUR *SKEPTICISM*. TO QUOTE RALPH HODGES, "SOME THINGS HAVE TO BE *BELIEVED IN* TO BE SEEN."

THIS ISN'T ABOUT *SKEPTICISM* OR *BELIEF*. IT'S ABOUT *STRATEGY*. WE'VE *FINALLY* GOT SOMETHING. THERE'S SUCH *STRONG* EVIDENCE, THE BUREAU *HAS* TO COOPERATE.

WHOEVER WE'RE UP AGAINST WILL BE LOOKING FOR *ANY* EXCUSE TO *DISCREDIT* US. ALL I'M SUGGESTING IS...WE DON'T *PROVIDE* ONE.

TO QUOTE THOMAS PYNCHON, "SO LONG AS THEY'VE GOT YOU ASKING THE WRONG *QUESTIONS*, THEY DON'T HAVE TO WORRY...

"...ABOUT THE *ANSWERS*."

TOUCHÉ.

AT LEAST THINK ABOUT IT. I'VE GOT TO GO. I HAVE AN *APPOINTMENT* WITH STUART GORDON, A *NEURO-SCIENTIST*.

I WANT TO GIVE HIM A *LOOK* AT THE *DATA*. MAYBE HE CAN MAKE MORE SENSE OF IT.

THE *ILBAL*: DOORWAY TO THE *UNKNOWN* OR EARLY AMERICAN *ACID* TRIP?

GUESS I'LL SEE WHAT I CAN LEARN ABOUT OUR *INTRUDER*.

ANY IDEAS?

YEAH... YOU'LL *LIKE* IT. IT'S... IT'S *MUNDANE*.

WHAT *BETTER* WAY TO *VANISH* BETWEEN HERE AND THE PARKING LOT THAN BY BEING AN *FBI* AGENT?

A MOLE?

ASK LAB DIVISION FOR HELP. AGENTS' MEDICAL RECORDS ARE ALL ON *FILE*.

MAYBE THEY CAN *MATCH* THE DNA FROM THE *BLOOD* SAMPLES.

IT HELPS IF YOU TRY TO TALK YOUR WAY THROUGH THE EXPERIENCE, DESCRIBE WHAT YOU'RE FEELING.

HELPS ME, OR HELPS YOU COLLECT DATA?

HAH! A BIT OF BOTH.

CLICK

SO FAR, DOCTOR GORDON, ALL I'M FEELING IS A LITTLE SILLY.

GIVE IT SOME TIME, AGENT SCULLY.

TEN MINUTES AND STILL NOTHING. I GUESS I'M JUST NOT A GOOD SUBJECT FOR...

WAIT A MINUTE. MY SKIN FEELS TINGLY.

AHHHH!

THE EFFECT I EXPERIENCED IN DR. GORDON'S LAB WAS PRODUCED BY ELECTRO-MAGNETIC WAVES.

THEORETICALLY, THERE'S NO REASON IT CAN'T BE TARGETED AND BROAD-CAST AT A DISTANCE.

IF HE HAS NATURALLY HIGH LABILITY, WHO KNOWS WHAT EFFECT SOMETHING LIKE THE ILBAL WOULD HAVE ON HIM.

THE ASSAILANT COULD BE ANY-ONE, CONTROLLED BY PERSONS UNKNOWN.

HEAVEN HELP ME, I'M THINKING LIKE MULDER.

MULDER.

JUDGMENTAL AND CREATIVE FITS MULDER TO A TEE.

SECURITY BREACH IN SECTION SEVEN. FOUR AGENTS, FIVE LAB PERSONNEL UNCONSCIOUS.

ALARM SYSTEM HAS BEEN *DISABLED*.

SEND *IMMEDIATE* BACKUP. SECURE THE FLOOR.

MULDER!

DON'T BOTHER!

HE CAN'T HEAR YOU.

A SWITCH I NEVER IMAGINED EXISTED HAS JUST BEEN CLICKED IN MY *HEAD*.

OBJECTS IN THE ROOM ARE NO LONGER *SIMPLE* THINGS.

EACH ONE SEEMS *ALIVE*. EACH ONE SPEAKS ITS *NAME*.

CHAIR SIT WOOD WALK FOREST LOST GRASS FEET HOME SLEEP EAT MOMMY.

EVERY WORD EVOKES AN IMAGE, SIGHT ON SIGHT, FEELING ON FEELING, LINKS IN A CHAIN THAT STRETCH ACROSS THE WHOLE OF MY LIFE.

I AM FEELING HOW MY BRAIN WORKS. I'M FEELING HOW *I* WORK. IT IS INTOXICATING.

AND THEN THERE'S SOMETHING MORE.

A VOICE THAT SAYS...

WELCOME TO THE BORDERLANDS.

THE LAST LIE REMAINING BETWEEN YOURSELF AND THE WORLD.

THIS IS MY FINAL REPORT AS AN AGENT FOR THE X-FILES DIVISION.

KNOWING THAT MY WORDS WILL BE SUBJECT TO INTENSE SCRUTINY BY BOTH THE BUREAU AND THE PUBLIC, MORE THAN EVER I FIND MYSELF ACUTELY AWARE OF MY OBLIGATION TO SET DOWN THE FACTS ACCURATELY.

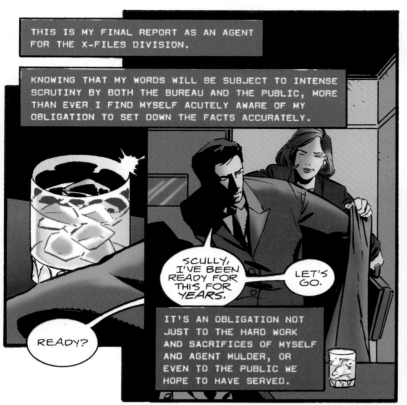

READY?

SCULLY, I'VE BEEN READY FOR THIS FOR YEARS.

LET'S GO.

IT'S AN OBLIGATION NOT JUST TO THE HARD WORK AND SACRIFICES OF MYSELF AND AGENT MULDER, OR EVEN TO THE PUBLIC WE HOPE TO HAVE SERVED.

IT IS ALSO AN OBLIGATION TO THE TRUTH.

SUCH OBLIGATIONS ARE NOT EASY TO FULFILL.

WHAT DO I KEEP? WHAT DO I FORGET? DO I MENTION THE NERVOUS FEAR IN MY HEART AS WE WALKED DOWN THE HALL OR THE FEEL OF THE AIR VENTS AGAINST MY FACE?

HOW DO I ENCAPSULATE AND CONVEY (IN STATISTICS? A DIARY? BIO-CHEMICAL REACTIONS?)...

...THAT MOMENT WE STEPPED INTO THE LIGHT?

THEY WILL *CLAIM* THEIR INTENT WAS TO SERVE AND *PROTECT* THE UNITED STATES OF AMERICA. PERHAPS THAT'S WHAT THEY BELIEVE *THEMSELVES*.

THE *FACT* IS THEY'VE BECOME MORE *MASTERS* THAN SERVANTS, MORE *DECEIVERS* THAN PROTECTORS.

IN THE COURSE OF THEIR *SELF-IMPOSED* DUTIES, THEY HAVE STOLEN, *MURDERED*, AND DEFIED OUR CONSTITUTION ON A *DAILY* BASIS.

IN SHORT, THE MEMBERS OF *PROJECT AQUARIUS* ARE TRAITORS AND *CRIMINALS.* TODAY, AT LAST, I'M *CONFIDENT* THEY WILL BE *TREATED* AS SUCH.

THESE FILMS AND PHOTOS HAVE BEEN *CONFISCATED* FROM THEIR OFFICES.

BUT FILMS CAN BE *FAKED*.

PHOTOS *RETOUCHED*.

SO WE DON'T ASK YOU TO *BELIEVE* THEM.

INSTEAD, WE ASK THAT YOU BELIEVE *THIS*.

THE *BODY OF* AN ALIEN-HUMAN HYBRID.

SORRY *YOU* WON'T BE HERE WITH US.

WELL, I'LL *ALWAYS* BE HERE IN *SPIRIT.* YOU SHOULD PARDON THE PHRASE.

BUT THE OPPORTUNITY TO HEAD THE FIRST *PUBLIC* RESEARCH TEAM STUDYING *ALIEN DNA* WAS JUST TOO *TEMPTING.*

YOU DO REALIZE THERE'S A SCIENTIFIC *EXPLANATION* FOR ALL THIS, *DON'T* YOU?

IT'S JUST THAT MAYBE THE *BOUNDARIES* OF SCIENCE AREN'T *QUITE* WHERE I THOUGHT THEY WERE.

YEAH, I KNOW WHAT YOU *MEAN.*

MY *CAR KEYS* ARE NEVER WHERE I THINK THEY ARE, EITHER.

AGENT MULDER!

AGENT SCULLY!

EXACTLY 9:00 A.M.

WHERE THE HELL HAVE YOU BOTH BEEN FOR THE LAST *THREE* WEEKS?

WHAT?

AGENT JEFFRIES SAID HE SAW US WALK OUT *HERE* WITH COLLEEN-- THAT WAS THE LAST *HE* REMEMBERED.

QUARTZ CRYSTAL, I'LL BET. A PIECE OF THE *ILBAL.*

NOVEMBER 22, 1995
10:12 A.M.
FBI ACADEMY
QUANTICO,
VIRGINIA

A GREAT START, BUT *NOW* WHAT?

WE'VE SEEN POLTERGEISTS, VAMPIRES, ALIENS, AND ANY MANNER OF *BEAST* THAT GOES BUMP IN THE NIGHT.

BUT HOW DO YOU EVEN *BEGIN* TO DEAL WITH SOMETHING THAT CAN CONTROL YOUR BODY *AND* ALTER YOUR MEMORY?

WHAT I SAW AT DOCTOR GORDON'S LAB* CONVINCED ME THE MIND CAN HAVE DIFFICULTY DISTINGUISHING BETWEEN FACT AND FICTION.

BUT THERE MUST BE *LIMITS* TO THE EFFECT.

*LAST ISSUE.

SUBCONSCIOUSLY, WE WERE BOTH EASY *PREY* FOR THAT *PARTICULAR* FANTASY.

I WONDER IF SHE HAD TO GIVE US *EVERYTHING* WE WANTED-- TO MAKE US FORGET WHATEVER *REALLY* HAPPENED HERE.

IT WOULD'VE BEEN THE *SECOND* TIME THIS WEEK.

WHAT?

NEVER MIND. NOTHING. I THINK YOU'RE *RIGHT* THE PIECES OF THAT FANTASY MIGHT HAVE *ALREADY* BEEN IN OUR MINDS.

I SHOULD TELL HER.

IF ONLY BECAUSE THE INFORMATION MIGHT HELP US WITH THE CASE. IF ONLY BECAUSE I TRUST HER WITH MY LIFE.

BUT I *DON'T* TELL HER.

STILL, JUDGING FROM HER REACTION, SOME UNCHECKED EMOTION MUST HAVE MADE ITS WAY TO MY *FACE*.

AFTER AN AWKWARD SILENCE, SHE ASKS...

MULDER? ARE YOU ALL RIGHT?

SO I PUT ON MY BEST GRIN AND SAY...

YEAH.

I'LL TELL YOU ABOUT IT SOME TIME.

BUT I'M NOT ALL RIGHT. I'M NOT ALL RIGHT AT ALL.

I'M STUCK IN A VERY *DARK* PLACE, WITH AN EVEN *DARKER* QUESTION.

IS MEMORY *REAL?*

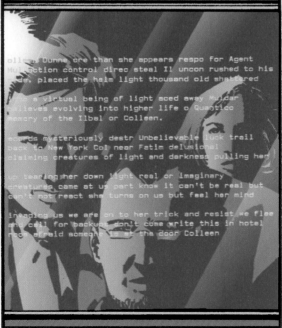

"DO YOU SEE IT, SCULLY?"

"YES. I'LL GET THE *TICKETS*. *YOU* TALK TO SKINNER."

OUR LADY OF FATIMA
BROOKLYN, NEW YORK
MONDAY, NOVEMBER 27, 1995
2:12 P.M.

SECURE THE PERIMETER AND KEEP THOSE *TRANQUILIZER* GUNS READY. YOU'VE GOT THE *DESCRIPTION*.

HEARD YOU PUT YOURSELF ON THE LINE FOR *THIS*, MULDER.

DON'T WORRY, WE WON'T *MISS*.

THIS IS YOUR *THIRD* VISIT THIS YEAR, AGENTS, AND EVERY TIME YOU'VE GIVEN ME CAUSE TO *REGRET* YOUR PRESENCE.

THIRD?

WE'RE LOOKING FOR *COLLEEN DUNNE*, FATHER. SHE'S RESPONSIBLE FOR SEVERAL *MURDERS*.

THE WOMAN *I* KNOW BY THAT NAME IS *INCAPABLE* OF CARING FOR *HERSELF*, MUCH LESS HARMING OTHERS.

SHE'S A DEEPLY *WOUNDED* SOUL, TOUCHED BY THINGS BEYOND HER *UNDERSTANDING* OR *CONTROL*.

SHE'S FINALLY FOUND *SANCTUARY* HERE. *RESPECT* THAT.

IT'S *ALL RIGHT*, FATHER.

YOU'RE SO AFRAID OF *FORGETTING*, SO *AFRAID* OF WHAT YOU DON'T KNOW THAT YOU HAVE NO IDEA WHAT A BLESSING IT IS NOT TO KNOW, WHAT A BLESSING IT IS TO FORGET.

MY BRAIN WAS OVERWHELMED.

BUT HOW TO PROTECT MYSELF FROM CAPTURE? THE SOLUTION WAS SIMPLE.

ALL I WANTED WAS TO WAKE UP, TO FIND A SINGLE *TRUTH* THAT FELT *REAL*, RATHER THAN FACE THE BILLION EQUAL *SHADOWS* THAT PUMMELED ME *DAILY*.

TO SAVE MYSELF, I NEEDED ACCESS TO THE *EXTREMES* OF EXPERIENCE. WHO BETTER EQUIPPED TO HELP ME THAN MY *CAPTORS?*

THE *RISKS* AROUSED *SUSPICION*, SO YOU WERE LED TO NEOLA. BY THE TIME THEY FOUND MY *SON*, I COULDN'T *SAVE* HIM WITHOUT EXPOSING *MYSELF*.

HE COULDN'T RETURN YOUR *SISTER*, MULDER ...THOUGH PERHAPS HE *THOUGHT* HE *COULD*.

I WISH I COULD HAVE FELT *SOMETHING* WHEN HE DIED.

BUT DON'T YOU SEE? THE SIMPLEST TRUTHS YOU TAKE FOR GRANTED ARE THE GREATEST MYSTERY TO ME. IS THIS *ROOM* REAL? ARE THESE LIGHTS ON MY FACE REAL? AM *I* REAL?

I WANTED TO SPEAK TO THE FIREBIRD AND ASK IT HOW TO SAVE MYSELF, BUT ITS ONLY *THOUGHTS* WERE OF *HOME*.

I SENT *DRAKE* TO KILL YOU, HOPING THEY'D MISTAKE HIM FOR *ME*, BUT HE FAILED.

AND FOR ALL I KNOW, HE'S STILL ON THAT SLED, FOREVER HEADED TOWARDS HIS DEATH.

I USED THEM. A GENERAL HERE, A BUREAUCRAT THERE. SINCE THEY WERE ALREADY IN A CONSPIRACY --IT WAS EASY TO MAKE THEM BELIEVE IN ANOTHER.

WITH THEM, I FORMED PROJECT AQUARIUS. YOU'D BE SURPRISED HOW EASY IT IS TO CREATE SOMETHING THAT NO ONE IS SUPPOSED TO KNOW ABOUT.

AND FOR FIVE DECADES, I SEARCHED THE POSSI-BILITIES, GROWING MORE DESPERATE WITH EACH PASSING DAY.

PERHAPS I MADE A MISTAKE WHEN I TURNED TO THE FATIMA PROPHECY. I TOOK GREAT RISKS TO PROCURE IT, AND WHAT IT SAID DEPRESSED ME UNUTTERABLY.

SOME FOUND SALVATION IN IT, BUT TO ME IT SAID, "SORRY, THE DEVOUT HAVE ALREADY BEEN TAKEN TO HEAVEN. THIS THING YOU THINK IS THE EARTH IS REALLY HELL."

ANGRY, I SHATTERED IT. MY TENUOUS GRASP ON THE WORLD LOOSENED. MY ABILITIES WERE FADING.

I DID WHAT I COULD TO PROTECT MYSELF, THEN CAME HERE.

WHY? TO APOLOGIZE FOR HAVING GROWN SO LARGE, I SUPPOSE, TO BEG TO BE MADE SMALL AGAIN.

TO ASK, OF ANYTHING THAT MIGHT BE LISTEN-ING, FOR ONE LAST EXCEPTION. TO ASK TO BE FREE OF MY HELL.

WILL IT SAVE ME? I DON'T KNOW. MAYBE IF I STARE AT THE LIGHT LONG ENOUGH, I'LL KNOW IF IT'S REAL OR NOT-- OR AT LEAST IT MIGHT STRIKE ME BLIND.

THE ILBAL WAS MY LAST CHANCE. LIKE MOCTEZUMA, I'D HOPED IT WOULD LEAD ME TO A HIGHER WORLD.

INSTEAD, IT ONLY MAGNIFIED MY PAINS.

COLLEEN DUNNE HAS YET TO SPEAK AGAIN. WE'LL PROBABLY NEVER KNOW EVERYTHING THAT HAPPENED TO US DURING THOSE MISSING DAYS.

AND WITH OUR ONLY WITNESSES A DYING CANNIBAL AND A SCHIZOPHRENIC WHO MAY HAVE MANIPULATED EARTH'S MOST POWERFUL GOVERNMENT AS THOUGH IT WERE A DIME STORE PUPPET...

WASHINGTON, DC
6:23 P.M.
DECEMBER 6, 1995

...THERE IS NO CASE. THERE WILL BE NO TRIAL.

USUALLY AT TIMES LIKE THESE... IN SPITE OF MY BEST INTENTIONS AT OPTIMISM... MY MIND WANDERS DOWN A PARTICULARLY DARK, BUT NOW FAMILIAR PATH.

IT ALWAYS BEGINS WITH SELF-DOUBT.

IT ALWAYS ENDS WITH DOUBTS ABOUT THE WORLD.

I SHOULD BE FILLED WITH RAGE AND FRUSTRATION.

BUT I'M NOT.

BECAUSE I BELIEVE COLLEEN DUNNE WAS WRONG.

US.

WE ARE THE TRACES OF THE PAST. WE ARE THE TRACES OF THE TRUTH.

I AM THE PRODUCT OF WHAT HAPPENED TO SAMANTHA.

AND I'LL FOLLOW THAT THREAD, NO MATTER HOW SLIM, UNTIL IT CONNECTS TO ANOTHER AND ANOTHER, UNTIL ONE DAY I DO FIND OUT WHAT HAPPENED TO HER.

IF IT TAKES THE REST OF MY LIFE.

AND TRUTH IS OUT THERE.

AND IT DOES LEAVE TRACES BEHIND.

THREE STEPS *FORWARD,* THREE STEPS *BACK,* HUH?

WELL, AT LEAST NOW WE HAVE A *SCIENTIFIC* EXPLANATION FOR *ABDUCTION* EXPERIENCES.

DON'T BE SO *SURE.*

SURE, SLEEP PARALYSIS AND TEMPORAL LOBE LABILITY MAY EXPLAIN *SOME* ABDUCTIONS.

BUT GIVEN THE PHYSICAL EVIDENCE...

...CORROBORATIVE SIGHTINGS...

...AND MULTIPLE ABDUCTIONS, IT CERTAINLY DOESN'T EXPLAIN THEM *ALL.*

STILL, IF IT WASN'T FOR YOU, WE NEVER WOULD HAVE *RECOVERED* THOSE COMPUTER FILES.

AND WHETHER YOU KNOW IT OR NOT, YOU'VE HELPED ME WITH A FEW *OTHER* THINGS, TOO.

AND SO... A SLIGHTLY *EARLY* XMAS GIFT.

THANKS, MULDER.

I *THINK.*

"HE WHO DOES NOT REMEMBER THE PAST IS..." OOPS. I FORGOT THE REST OF THE QUOTE!

ANYWAY, IT'S NICE TO SEE YOU MORE *CHEERFUL.*

YEAH, WELL.

IT'S A TOUGH JOB.

BUT SOME-BODY'S GOT TO DO IT.

THE END

TRUST NO ONE

CHIP CHIP
WHIRR
WHIRR
CRUNCH
CRUNCH.

THERE
THEY GO.
AT IT
AGAIN.

CHIP CHIP
WHIRR
WHIRR
CRUNCH
CRUNCH.

YOU'D THINK
I WAS A
CURE FOR
ALL ILLS OR
A PIECE OF
GOD'S LOVE.
BUT I'M
NOT.

CHIP CHIP
WHIRR
WHIRR
CRUNCH
CRUNCH.

BEEN AT IT
NOW FOR
TWO
HUNDRED
YEARS.

CHIP CHIP
WHIRR
WHIRR
CRUNCH.
CRUNCH.

BUT I'M
BURIED SO
DEEP I'LL
NEVER BE
FOUND.

CHIP CHIP
WHIRR
WHIRR
CRUNCH.
CRUNCH.

EXCEPT BY
YOU. YOU'LL
COME GET
ME *SOON,*
WON'T YOU?

CHIP CHIP
WHIRR
WHIRR
CRUNCH.
CRUNCH.

THE
PIT

3:27 P.M.
NOVEMBER 15, 1995
OAK ISLAND
NOVA SCOTIA

GRGGGGG

MULDER, WE'VE GOT ABOUT *TEN FEET* TO GO.

IF WE GET THROUGH NICE AND *SLOW*, WITHOUT HIM *NOTICING*, WE'LL *GAS* HIM, SO KEEP HIM *TALKING* AND KEEP THAT *MASK* HANDY!

I'M *GLAD* THE FBI WAS INVITED TO ASSIST IN THIS HOSTAGE SITUATION, EVEN THOUGH THIS IS A LITTLE OUT OF YOUR *JURISDICTION*, AGENT *SCULLY*. THIS PIT HAS A STRANGE HISTORY.

AND WE HAVE A LOT OF EXPERIENCE IN INVESTIGATING STRANGE THINGS.

YOU CAN'T *TALK* TO HIM! CAN'T Y-YOU SEE HE'S *INSANE!?*

SHUT UP, TRENT! THIS IS ALL *YOUR* FAULT FOR DIGGING HERE IN THE *FIRST* PLACE!

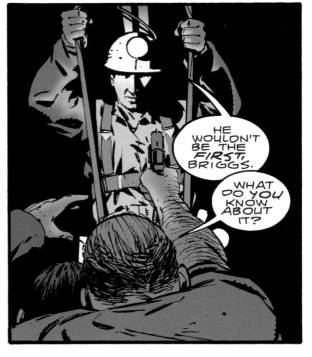

HE WOULDN'T BE THE *FIRST*, BRIGGS.

WHAT DO *YOU* KNOW ABOUT IT?

"I KNOW QUITE A BIT ABOUT THE OAK ISLAND MONEY PIT. IN 1795, WHEN DANIEL MCGINNIS AND HIS FRIENDS STARTED DIGGING IN A SMALL DEPRESSION HERE, THEY FOUND OAK PLATFORMS.

"AFTER THIRTY FEET, THEY NEEDED HELP, BUT THERE WERE NO TAKERS. EVERYONE KNEW THE ISLAND WAS HAUNTED. THE YEAR EARLIER, A BOATLOAD OF MEN INVESTIGATING THE STRANGE LIGHTS SEEN ON THE ISLAND NEVER RETURNED."

"YES! THE LIGHTS! I SAW THOSE LIGHTS!"

"IN 1804, THEY FOUND CHARCOAL, COCONUT FIBER, AND A STONE WITH A CIPHER ON IT. AT 98 FEET, THEY HIT WHAT MAY HAVE BEEN A CHEST, THEN THE TUNNEL FLOODED.

"IN 1849, A NEW GROUP BROUGHT UP A FEW LINKS FROM A WATCH CHAIN--AND, POSSIBLY, A JEWEL, WHICH VANISHED WITH THE FOREMAN WHO FOUND IT.

"WHEN THE PIT FILLED IN, THEY FOUND A FLOOD TUNNEL. IN 1859, THEY TRIED TO DRAIN IT WITH STEAM-POWERED PUMPS. WHEN THE BOILER BURST, SCALDING ONE OF THE MEN TO DEATH--THEY GAVE UP."

"YES! THEY HAD TO DIE, JUST LIKE TRENT!"

"OKAY. SLOW DOWN, BRIGGS. NOW, IN 1894, THE OAK ISLAND TREASURE COMPANY DESTROYED THE FLOOD TUNNEL WITH DYNAMITE. AT 150 FEET, THEY HIT A SECOND FLOOD TUNNEL. THE ONLY THING THEY FOUND WAS SOME PARCHMENT WITH THE LETTERS 'V. I' ON IT.

"A 1938 EFFORT REACHED AN UNDER-WATER CHAMBER AT 180 FEET. IN 1970, THE TRITON ALLIANCE SENT A CAMERA INTO THE CHAMBER. IT SHOWED THREE CHESTS AND A DISMEMBERED HAND. DIVERS WERE LOWERED IN -- BUT FOUND NOTHING.

"AND JUST LAST WEEK, YOUR BOSS... TRENT... UNCOVERED A LAYER OF IRON AT THE BOTTOM OF THAT CHAMBER."

"YES! TRENT MUST DIE! THEY WANT HIM!"

"EASY, BRIGGS."

INCAS, NORSEMEN-- NO ONE *KNOWS* WHO BUILT IT. THE POPULAR THEORY IS *PIRATES.*

THE COCO- NUT FIBER INDICATES WEST OR EAST INDIES-- NOTORIOUS HAUNTS OF *BUCCANEERS.*

THAT'S ALL I KNOW. CARE TO TELL ME WHAT *YOU* KNOW?

YOU WOULDN'T *BELIEVE* WHAT I KNOW.

I BELIEVE ALL *SORTS* OF THINGS. WHY DON'T YOU *TRY* ME? YOU WERE HIS *FOREMAN,* WEREN'T YOU?

"YEAH. IT WASN'T BAD ENOUGH WE WERE WORKING SEVEN DAYS A WEEK--SOON HE HAD US WORKING NIGHTS, TOO.

"WHAT WITH THE *FOG,* THERE MUST'VE BEEN A *HUNDRED* SAFETY ORDINANCES BEING VIOLATED, BUT TRENT NEVER CARED MUCH FOR *RULES.*

"SO MAYBE ONE DAY SOME- ONE FIGURED HE'D MAKE IT A *SHORT* NIGHT BY *SABOTAGING* THE GENERATOR.

"ALL THE LIGHTS *SHOULD'VE* GONE OUT.

"PROBLEM IS --A COUPLE *DIDN'T.*"

BRIGGS! I TOLD YOU THIS ISLAND WAS *HAUNTED!*

YOU SHOULD BE SO *LUCKY.*

I DON'T KNOW WHY I SHOULD *SHARE* THIS WITH *NEANDER- THALS...*

...BUT AS I *MEDITATED* THIS EVENING, I HAD A GREAT *VISION.*

I *SAW* WHAT LIES AT THE *BOTTOM.* IT *CALLED* TO ME. IT *WANTS* ME AS BADLY AS I WANT IT.

SO I'LL TOLERATE NO MORE PETTY *TRICKS*. REST WHEN I TELL YOU TO, OR I'LL *REPLACE* YOU ALL WITH CHIMPANZEES.

→CONNECT THE *BACK-UP* GENERATOR, BRIGGS.

I'D LIKE TO PUT THIS DRILL BIT THROUGH HIS CHEST.

EASY, TOM. THINK OF THE *MONEY* HE'S PAYING.

"I GAVE THE BOYS A TEN-MINUTE BREAK AND WE SET ABOUT TRYING TO GET THE *POWER* BACK.

"BUT I FELT SOMETHING AT MY BACK.

"FIRST, I THOUGHT IT WAS *TRENT* OR ONE OF THE OTHERS.

"BUT IT *WASN'T*.

"I'M NOT A *RELIGIOUS* MAN. HELL, I'M NOT EVEN AN *HONEST* MAN, BUT I SWEAR THOSE THINGS WERE *REAL*.

"AND THEY *WANTED* WHAT THEY'D WANTED FOR *HUNDREDS* OF YEARS. AND *WHAT THEY WANTED*, THEY WANTED *BADLY*.

"AND WHAT THEY *WANTED WAS...*"

THE END

HOTOGRAPHIC
EVIDENCE

CLASSI

TRUST NO ONE

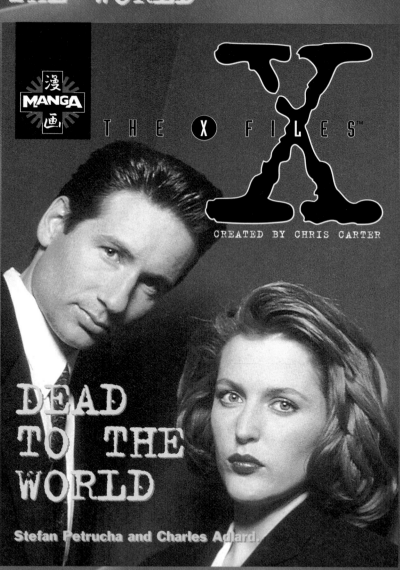